© JIŘÍ VOTRUBA

GOLEM

An Old Prague Tale

W9-CEK-186

Prague is a city made for fairy tales. And some fairy tales could never exist anywhere else...

Many, many years ago, during the reign of King Rudolph II, Prague started to become, in an age rightfully called the Age of Stars and Mandrakes, a city of science, art and magic.
One of the king's favorites, in addition to his astrologers, alchemists, charlatans and conjurors, was the wise rabbi Jehúdá Loew ben Becalel.

Few understood old books and cabbalas as well as he did. It was said that he knew secrets that nobody else knew and understood the way of life and the world better than anyone else. He suffered the hardships of the Jewish people and kept asking God how he could help his people.

One night, while Rabbi Loew was in a deep sleep, an angel appeared to him. "As the wisest of men, good rabbi, God has chosen you. He is placing in your hands the chance to save your unfortunate people and to help them overcome all adversities. The name of this hope is Golem." Using the wisdom of ancient books, Rabbi Loew could bring a big helper to life, an artificial human. "Only you will be his master, and he will be your servant."

While the city slept under the cover of a dark sky, a small group of the rabbí's most devoted pupils set off with their master to the river to gather clay. The time flowed by lazily like water under a bridge and the men filled up the boat with several bags of soft earth. The day of Golem's birth was approaching.

They went to work that very same night. With the clay, they lumped together a molded human form and fashioned eyes and nostrils; and by morning they were ready. The rabbi then asked his pupils to leave him alone. And at the break of dawn he brought Golem to life. Puffs of smoke issued from its nostrils; internal heat baked the clay to its body. Golem rose and Rabbi Jehúdá Loew ben Becalel was his only master.

After the rabbi commanded Golem to watch over the gates of the Jewish Quarter, not even a mouse could squeak through. Under the dark of night, Golem would appear where no one expected him to; and the Jewish people felt safer than they ever had felt before.

And because Golem was a good servant to his master, he fulfilled each of his commands. But what tasks should he have Golem do to keep him completely busy? After all, was there not enough work for one rabbi? Golem even helped out in his surroundings.

One day the rabbi's servant girl asked if Golem might help her carry the water. With his immense strength, however, Golem wasn't suited to light work. He put the whole fountain on his shoulders and suddenly half the square was under water.

Another time, instead of wood for the fire, he brought trees from the royal gardens, complete with their roots, leaned them up against the Queen's villa Belvedere and asked where to put them.

And when his work was finished, he went to a pub.
A Spanish general was sitting in the restaurant.
After hearing of the strong fellow next to him, he
resolved to recruit Golem for his army.

Secretly, he followed Golem from Old Town
across Charles' Bridge, Charles' Street,
Maiselova, all the way to the rabbi's
residence. And while he was lightly stepping
along the cobblestones of Prague, a plan
was forming in his head.

"I will give you all of my wealth for Golem, rabbi," said the Spaniard excitedly. But the wise rabbi knew the danger Golem could present if he fell into the hands of the wrong people. And so he not only refused to sell Golem, but decided it was best to destroy him.

From then on, Rabbi Jehúdá Loew ben Becalel again lived alone. In place of Golem, his pupils assisted him; and the rabbi embarked on the studies of mysterious books with a new fervor. His wisdom gradually took root in the land where he lived and he even once was connected with this land.

This was written in 1609, when Rabbi Loew departed our world and found his final resting place in Prague's Old Jewish Cemetery. To this day, throngs of people visit his grave and leave small stones on his gravestone. Sometimes tucked away among the stones is a scrap of paper written in all sorts of languages of this world. Notes with secret wishes are read by the curious wind or the spirit of Rabbi Loew. And on walkways everywhere around here, bits of dust swirl about from the bottom of the Vltava River, dust that long ago belonged to the body of a giant that was created to do good deeds.

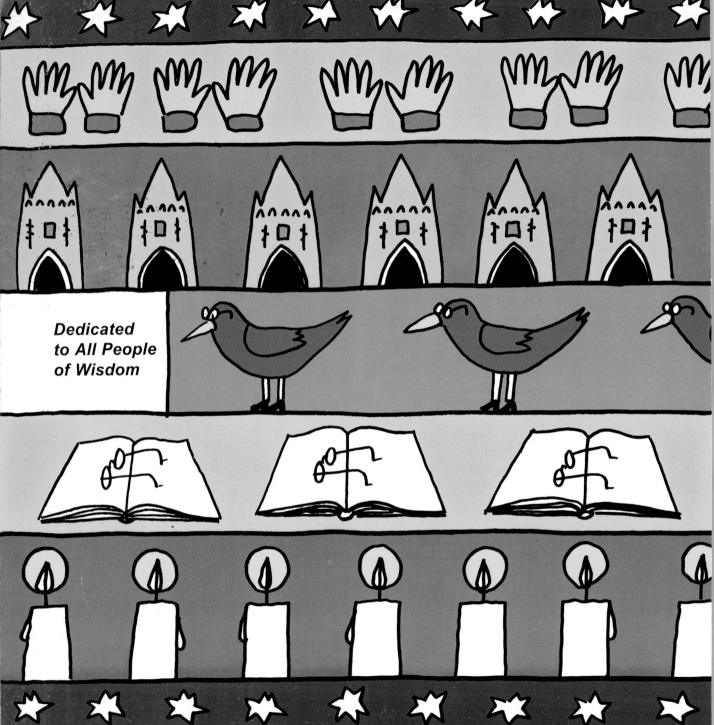

Dedicated
to All People
of Wisdom